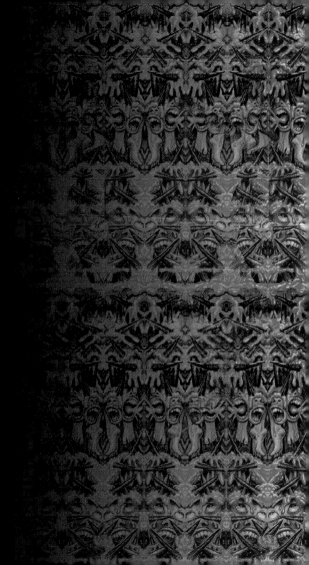

This edition first published by
JG Press, Inc., 1996
455 Somerset Avenue
No. Dighton, MA 02764

ISBN 1 57215 184 6

Printed and bound in Italy

3D Sterograms were created in Mystify 3D
courtesy of Oliver Fuhrer

Roger Kean and Oliver Frey

Abandon hope all ye who enter here!

Welcome to the stereogram pit of 3D despair! Some of the two-dimensional surface images in this blood-curdling book may even look pretty, but all of them mask your worst three-dimensional nightmares. Horrors to thrill and terrorize.

Most of you will know how to penetrate to the hidden image floating in 3D beneath the pattern on the page, but for the newcomers here are some quick tips to get to stereogram horror: In a quiet, well-lit place, sit and hold up the page level with and quite close to your eyes. Now focus as if you are looking at something much further away than the book you are holding. Relax and take in the out-of-focus pattern before you. Slowly move the page away from you, holding your distant focus, and soon the blurred pattern turns into

multi-layered shapes which form the hidden image.

Once you have caught a part of it, concentrate and let your eyes roam over the whole 3D object to view the detail. Gently altering the left-to-right angle of the book adds to the reality of the solid image.

As with all things practice makes perfect, and having successfully found and shuddered over a few hidden images you'll discover you can, with a little effort, see them even at a distance, in a crowded bookstore or through a window – or, perhaps, even under your bed. So shut the closet door and prepare to shiver. Here's what's in store on the following pages…

These are the hidden images you can find on the front cover (above), the back cover (right) and the previous page (top right).

If you have difficulty in seeing any of the other hidden images in this book, turn to page 36 – where we've been cruel to be kind...

9. Turn your gaze away from the gibbet and its victim
10. Avoid the eyes of the vampire
11. Beware the jaws of death
12. Your very own close encounter
13. Unlucky for some, especially the explorer who finds the pit
14. If you're not careful you could find this page turns you batty
15. A-maze your family and friends with an endless nightmare
16. Vlad The Impaler ensures his prisoners get the point
17. Don't go near the haunted house
18. The Four Horsemen of the Apocalypse ride out
20. What goes up, must come down...
21. We all have one of these tucked away in the cupboard
22. On a moonlit night, stay clear of the werewolf
23. Cry "sanctuary" for the Hunchback

of Notre Dame
24. Mount your broomstick and weave some magic
25. Take some nuts and bolts and blend together with human flesh
26. The tentacled monster from the deep is hungry
27. Flee from the mighty King of the Jungle
28. Disobey the warning of page 17, and you could meet this ghostly being
29. Bow down before Satan triumphant
30. Shrink from the multi-armed Kali, goddess of death
32. This is no time to be playing "Chopsticks" on the piano
33. Horror lurks under every floorboard
34. If you can't get out of the endless maze, be ready for the Minotaur
35. If you can see all these 3D images, a howl of anguish may be your only sensible reaction

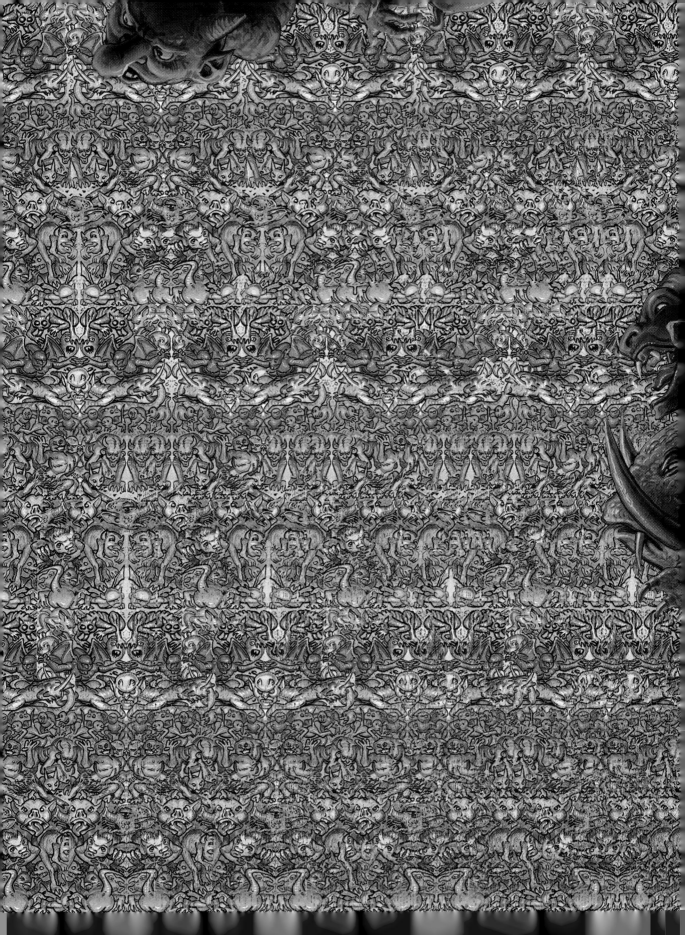

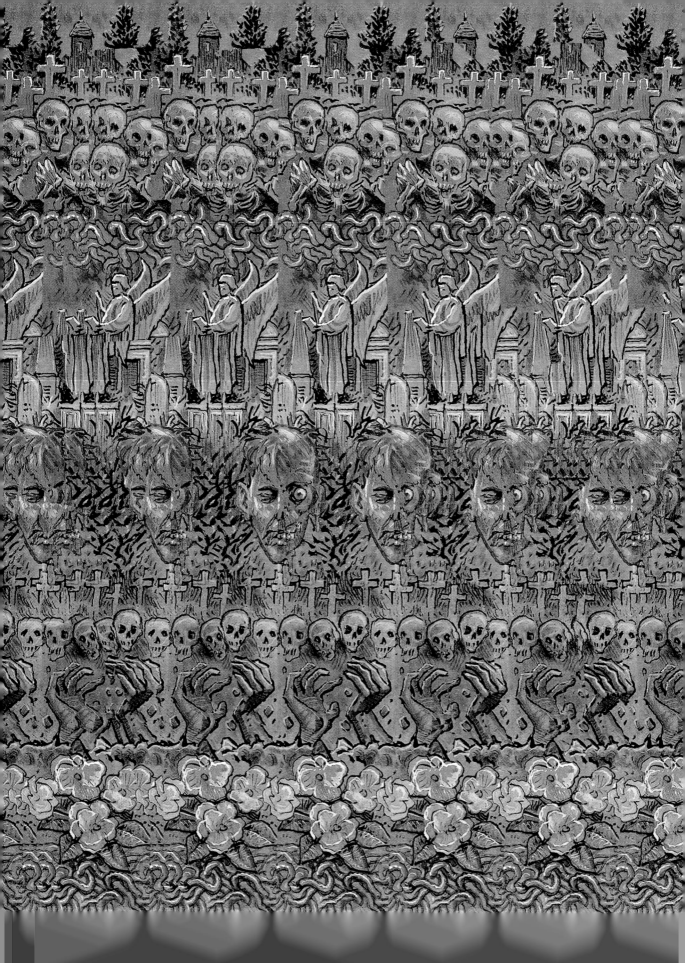

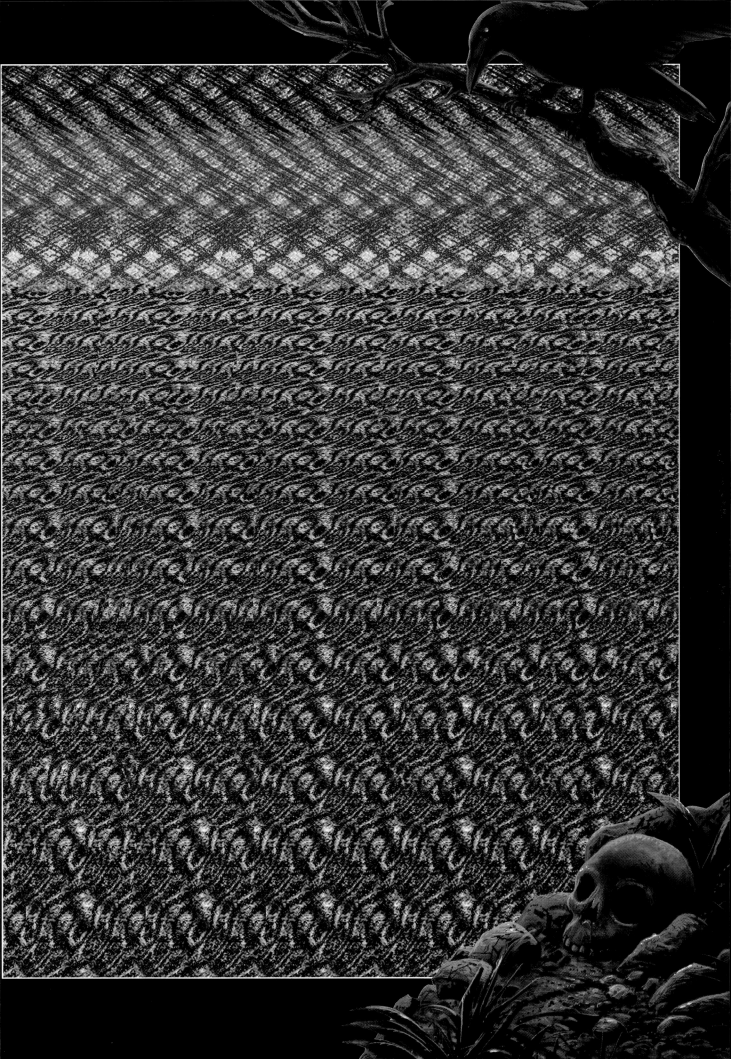

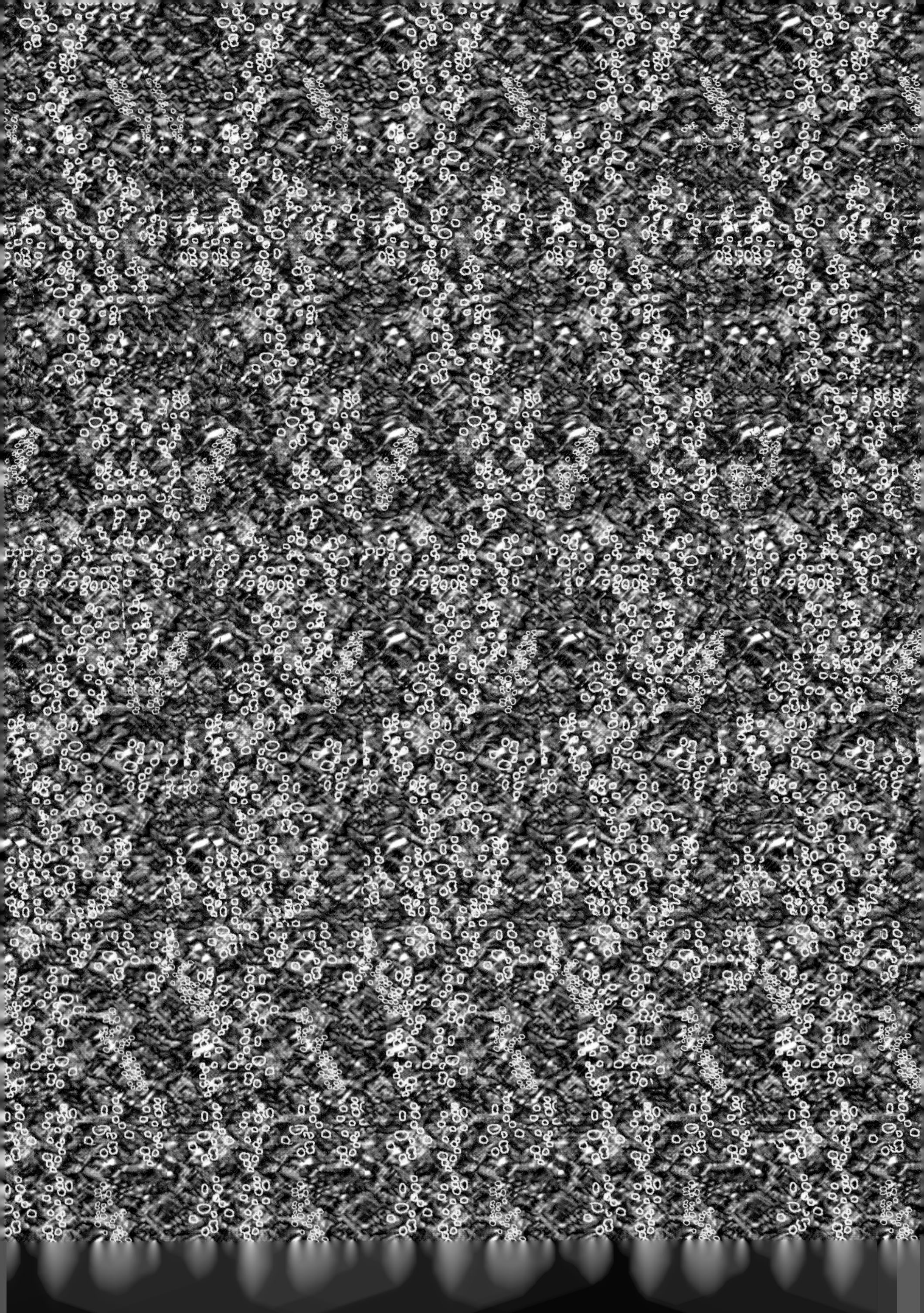

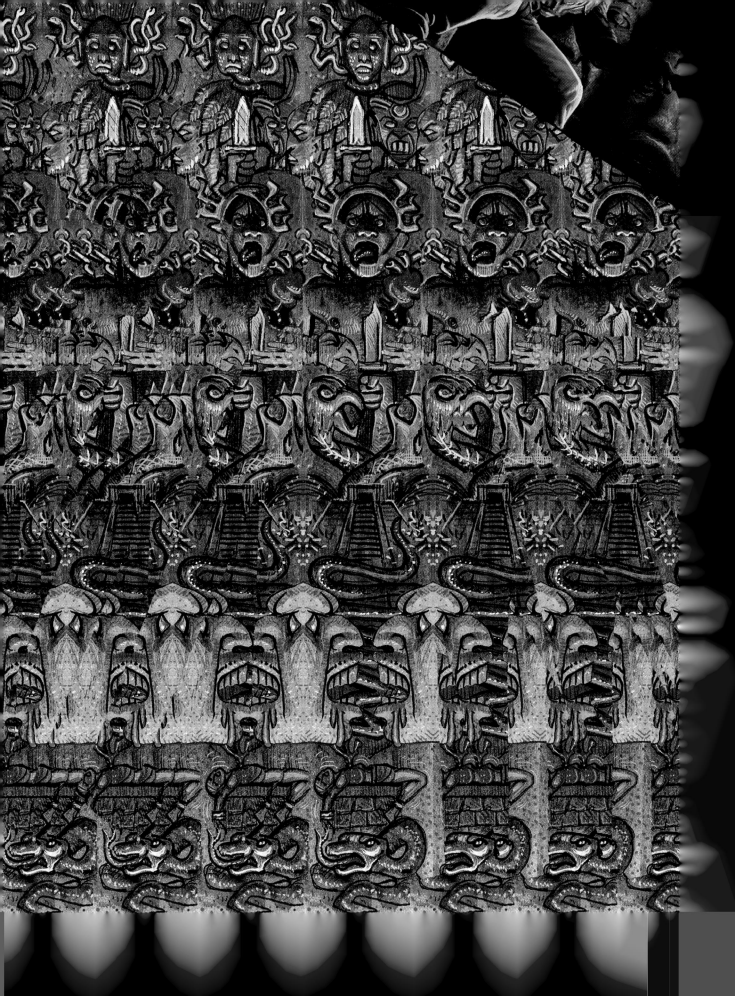

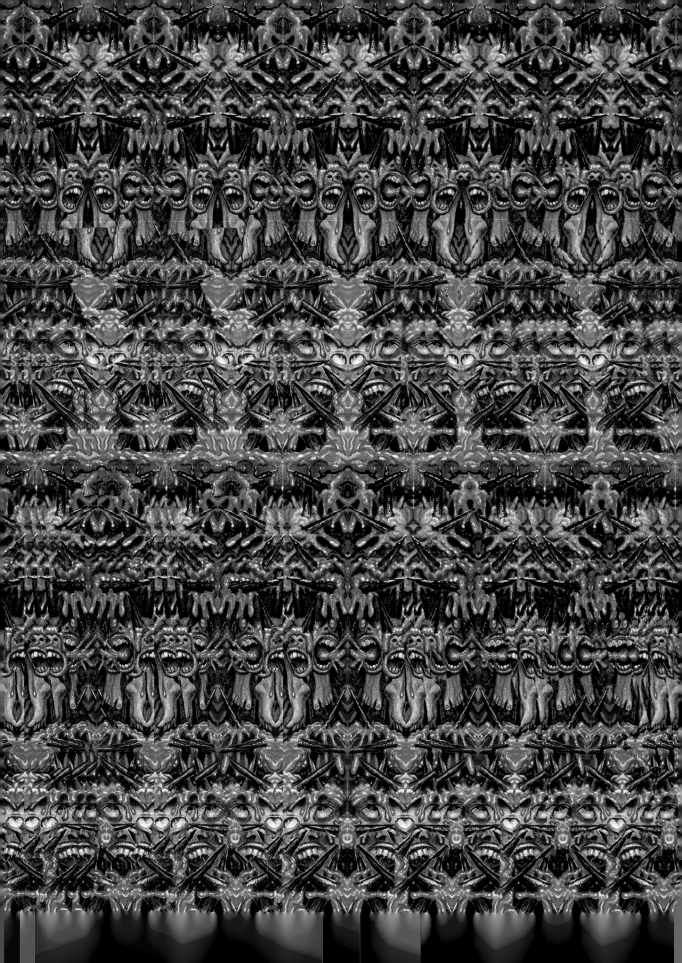

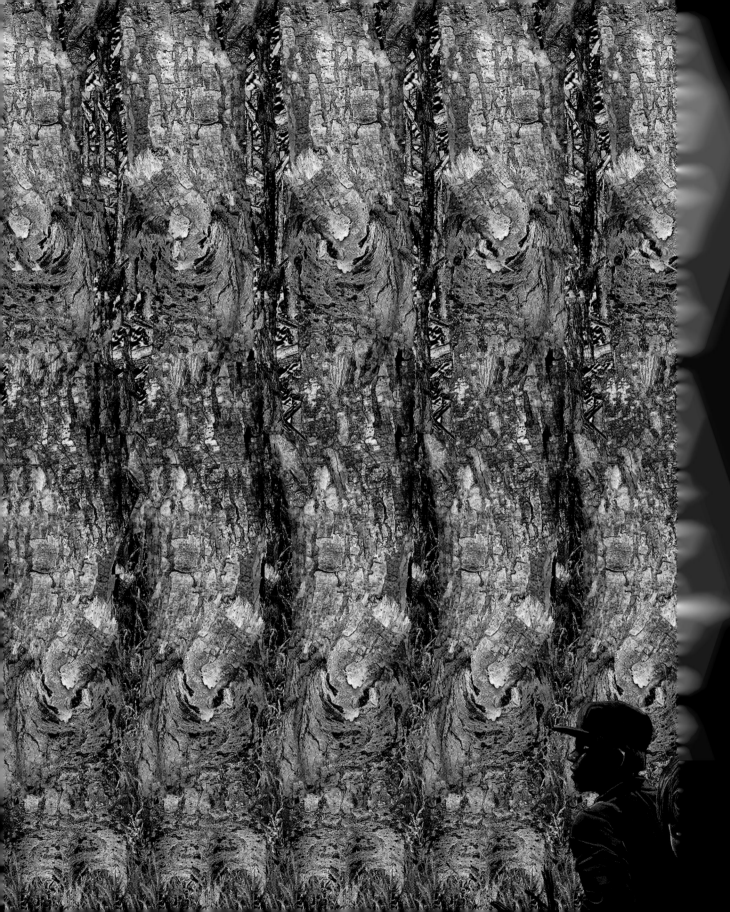

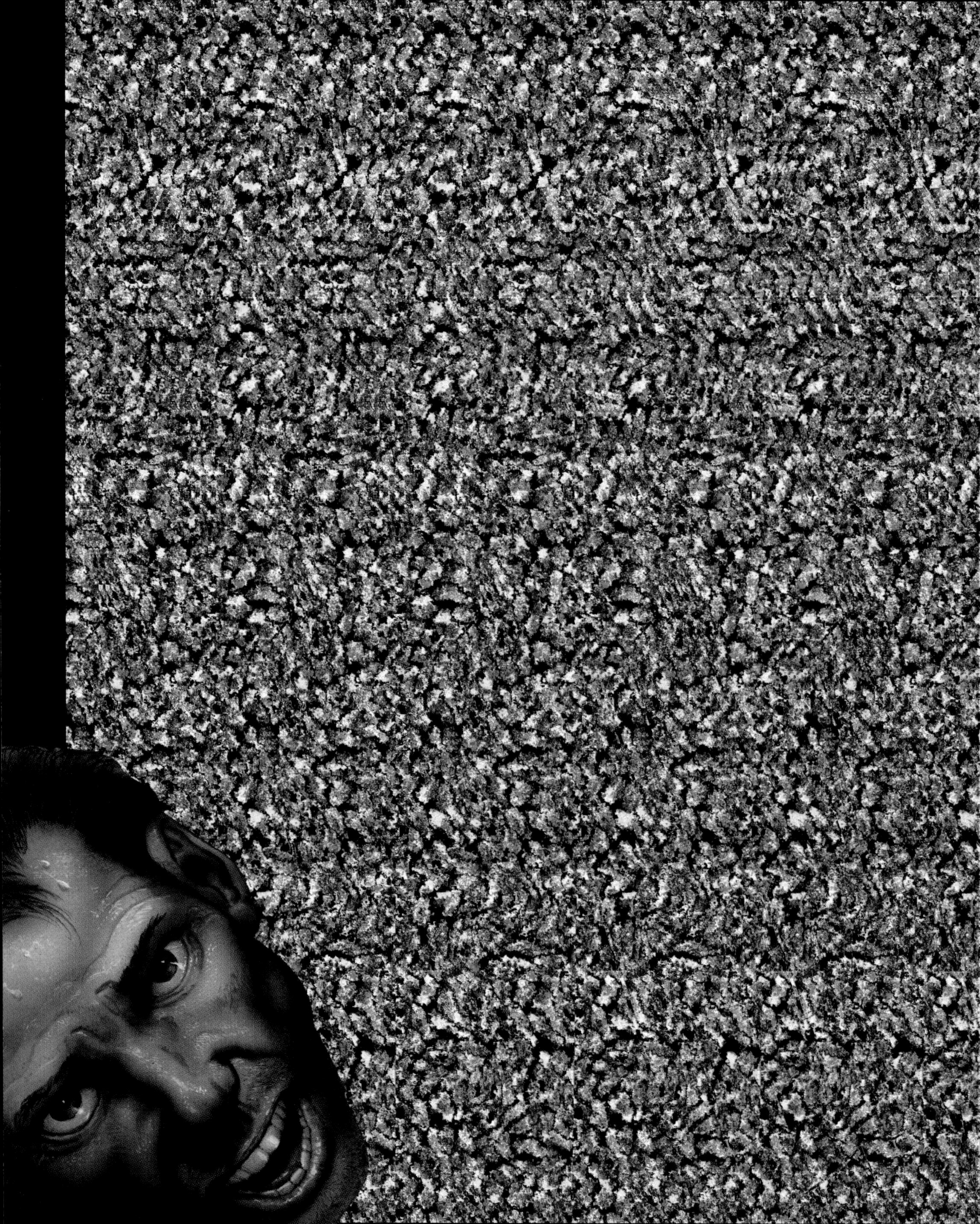

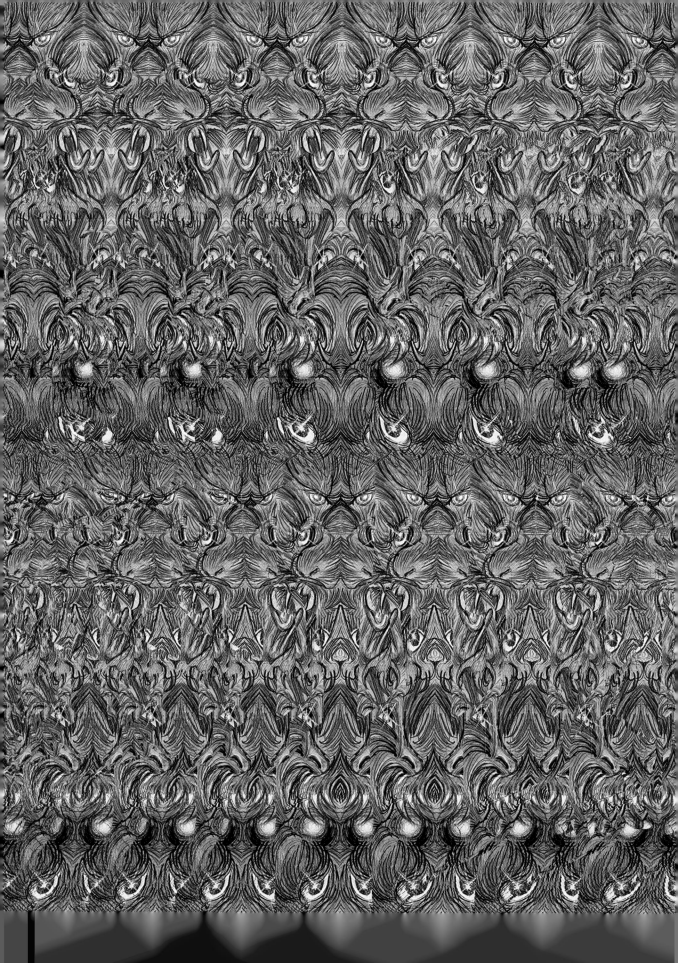

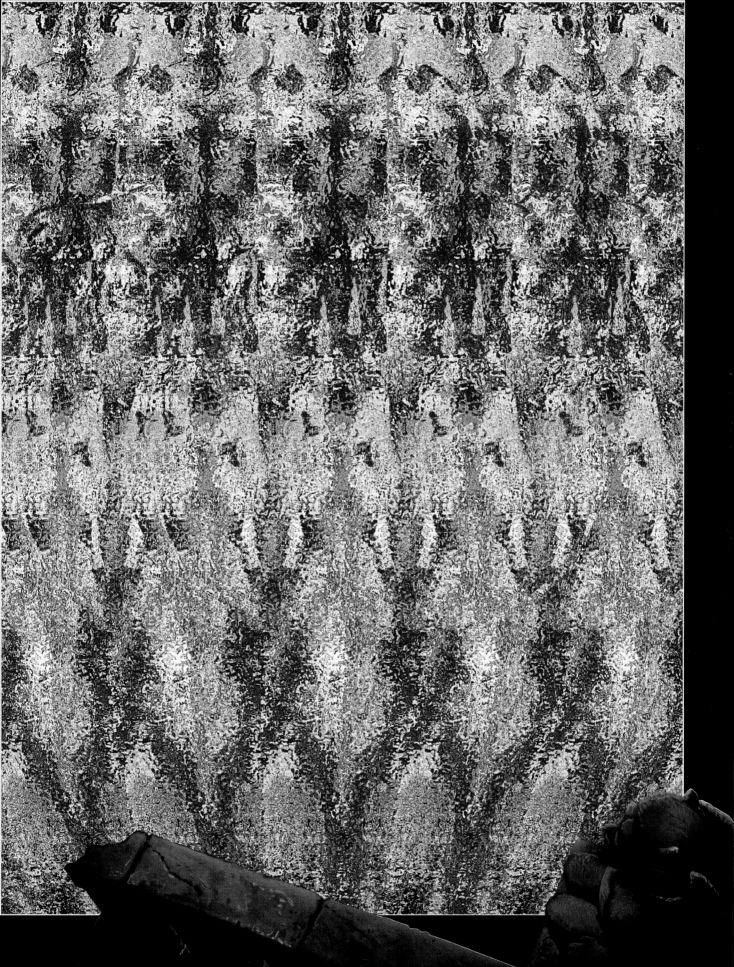

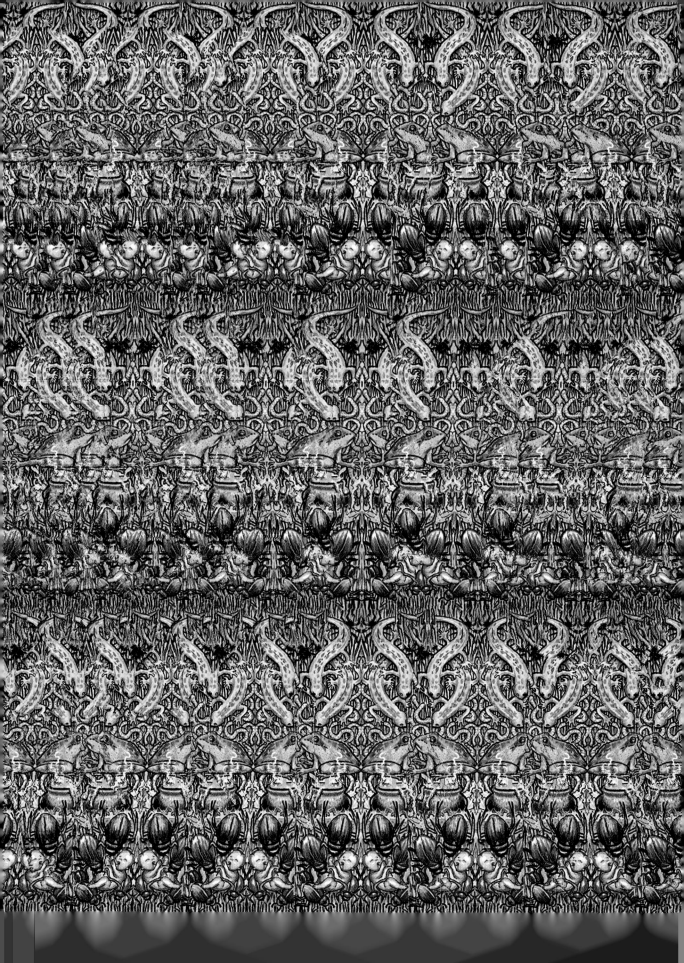

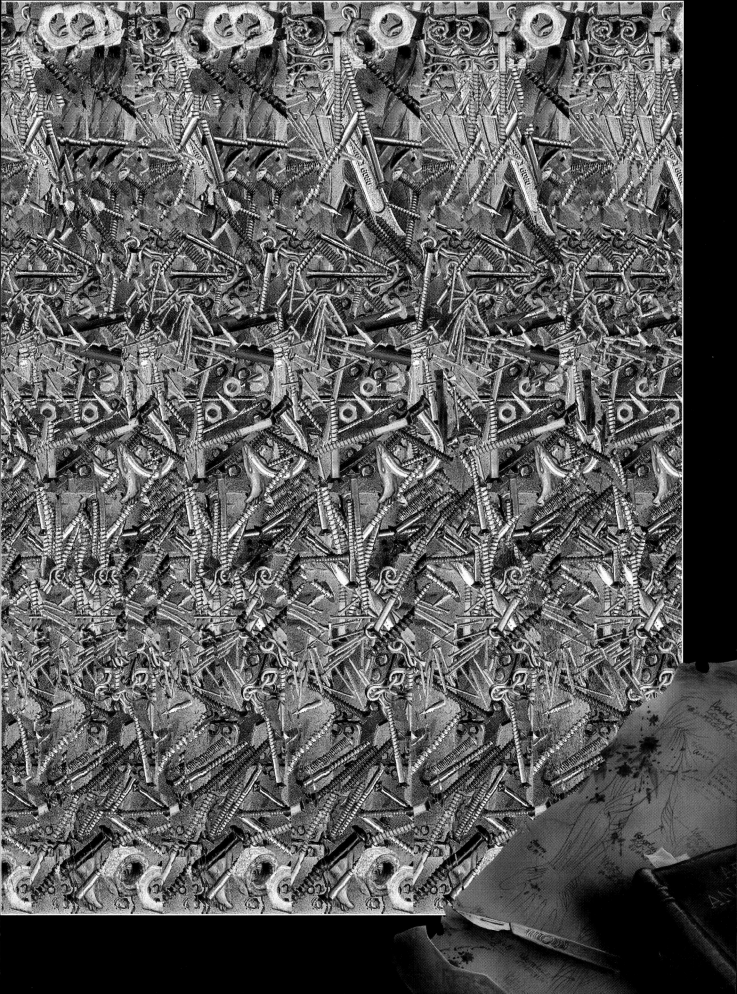

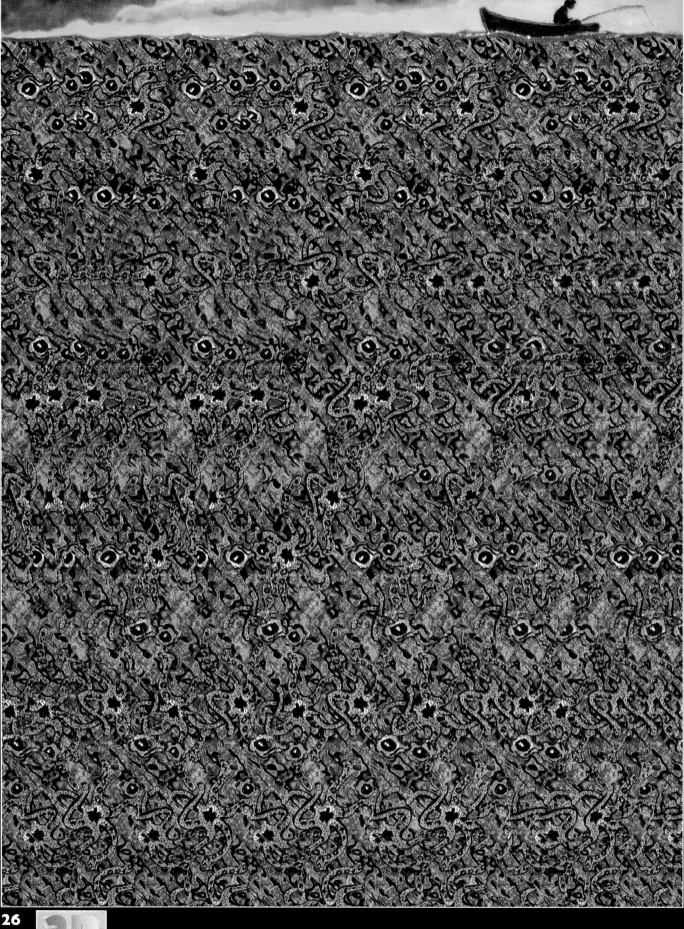

3D

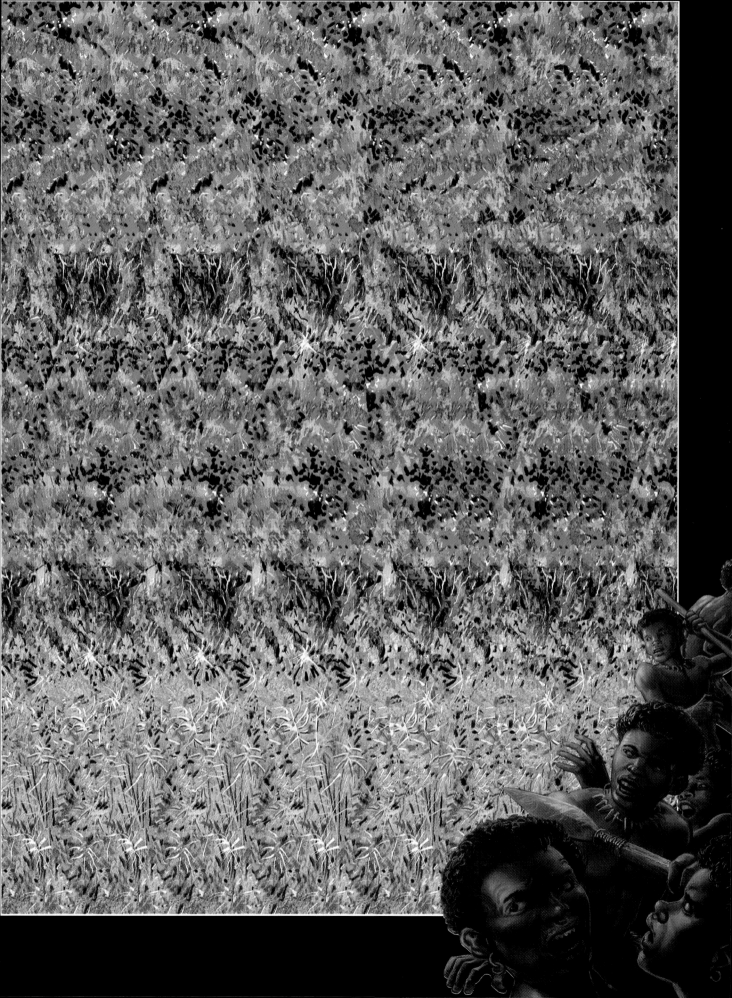

3D

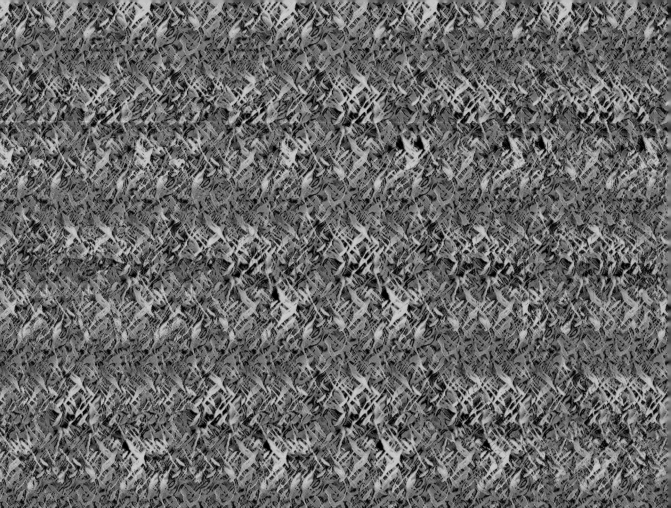

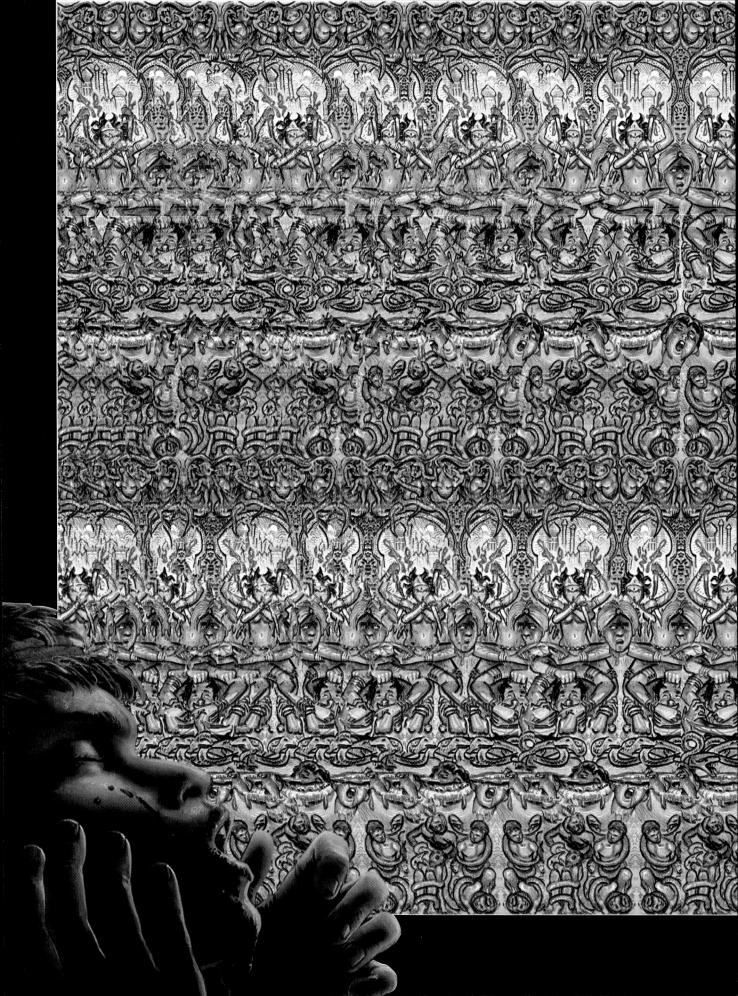

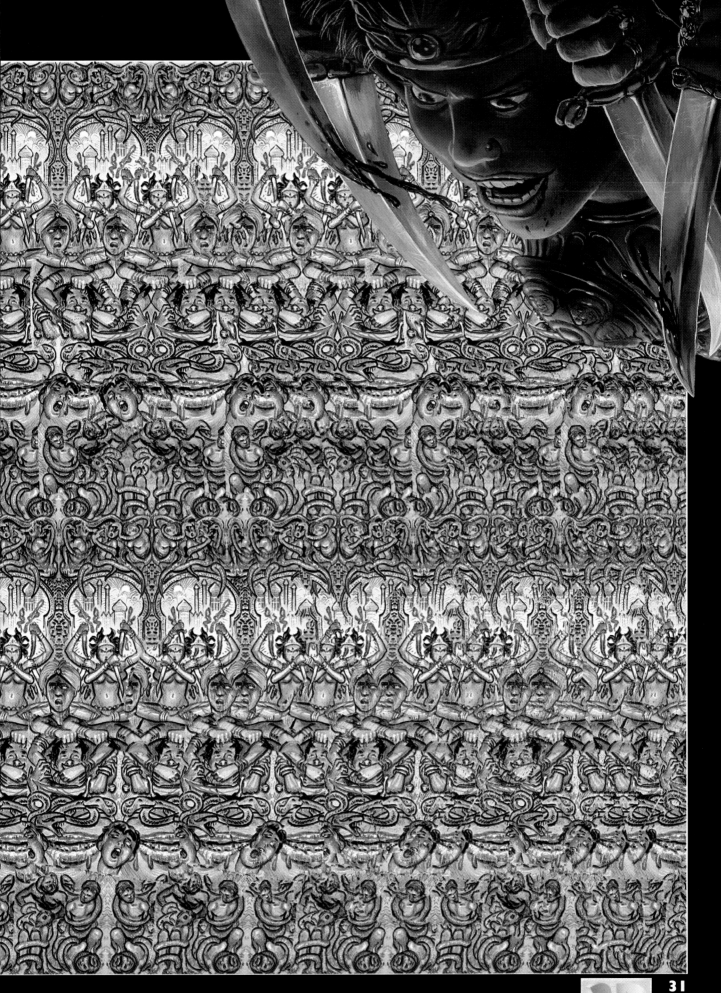

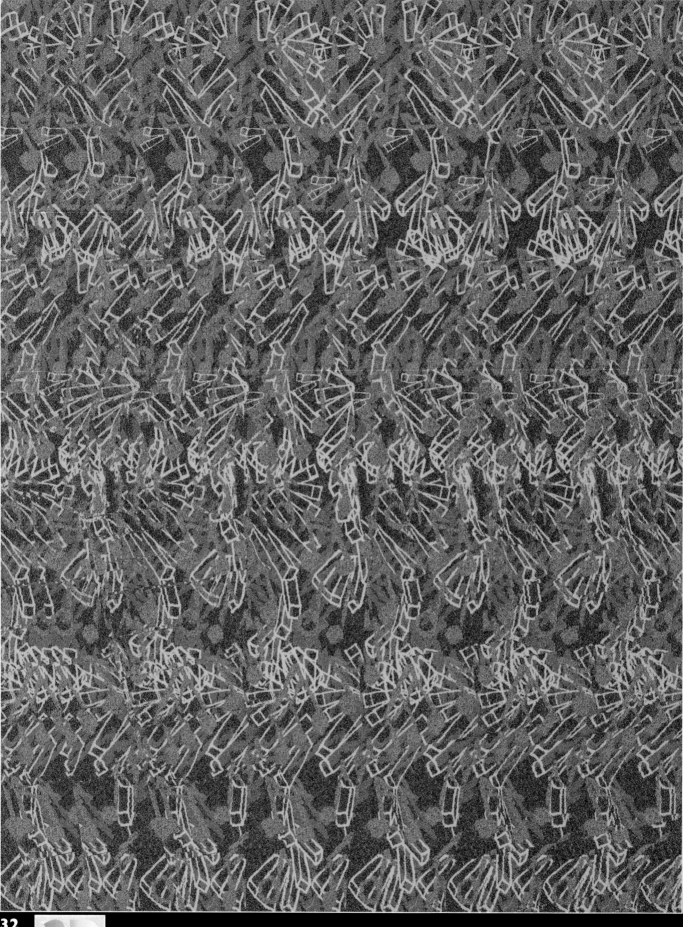

3D

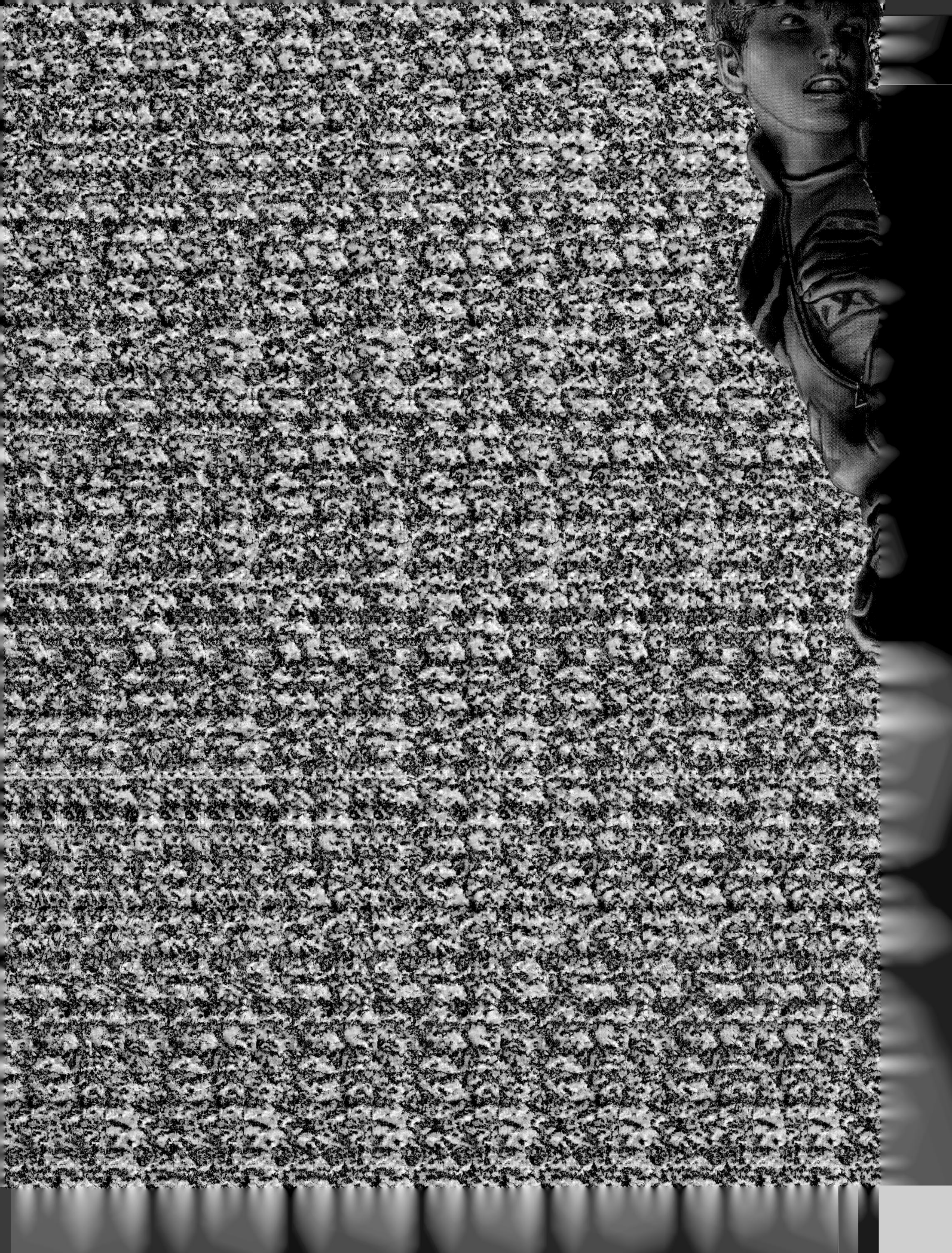

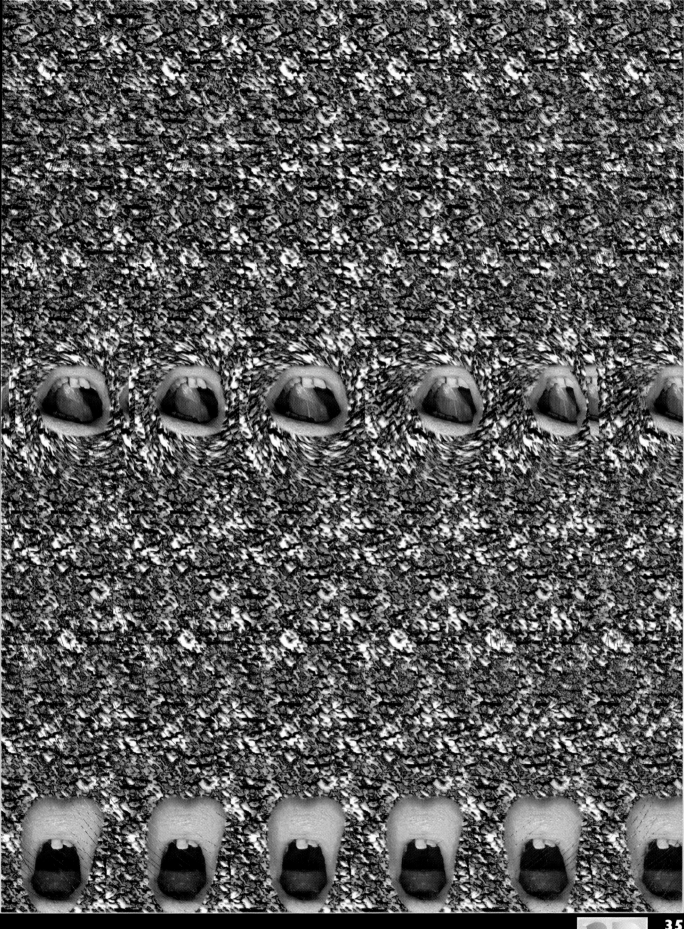

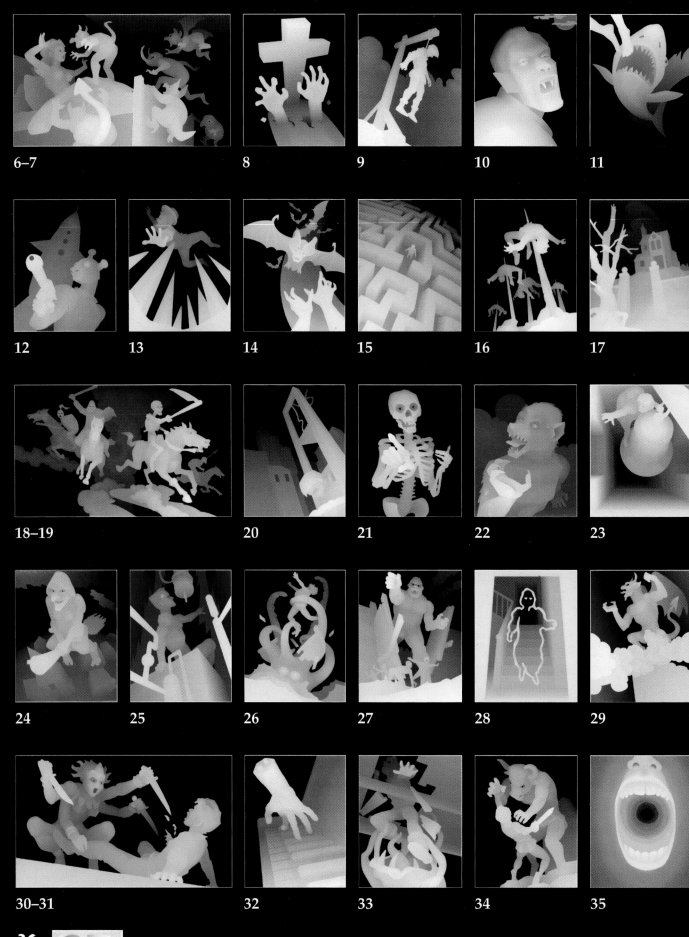

6–7

8

9

10

11

12

13

14

15

16

17

18–19

20

21

22

23

24

25

26

27

28

29

30–31

32

33

34

35

3D